Teacher Edition

Kind and Brave

by
Laurel Hicks

A Beka Book® Reading Program

A Beka Book®
A MINISTRY OF
PENSACOLA CHRISTIAN COLLEGE
PENSACOLA, FLORIDA 32523-9160

A Beka Book ® ⬟ Reading Program

Handbook for Reading *(grades 1–3)*
Primary Bible Reader *(grades 1–3)*
Read & Think Skill Sheets *(grades 3–6)*

1st

Fun with Pets
Tiptoes
Stepping Stones
Secrets and Surprises
The Bridge Book
Open Windows
Kind and Brave
Aesop's Fables
Strong and True

2nd

Story Tree
Treasure Chest
Hidden Treasure
No Longer a Nobody *(novel)*
Paths of Gold
Sunshine Meadows
Silver Sails
All Things—Even Frisky *(novel)*
Growing Up Where
   Jesus Lived
All Kinds of Animals

3rd

Paths to Adventure
Footprints
Crossroads
Pilgrim Boy *(novel)*
Secret in the Maple Tree *(novel)*
Better Bridges
Worlds of Wonder
Pilgrim's Progress

4th

Song of the Brook *(novel)*
Saved at Sea *(novel)*
Salute to Courage
Liberty Tree
Flags Unfurled
Trails to Explore
Adventures in Other Lands
   (Speed/Comprehension)

5th

Rosa *(novel)*
Noah Webster: A Man Who
   Loved Words
Beyond the Horizon
Windows to the World
Of America 1
Adventures in Nature
   (Speed/Comprehension)

6th

Billy Sunday
Message of the Mountain *(novel)*
Mountain Pathways
Voyage of Discovery
Of America II
Adventures in Greatness
   (Speed/Comprehension)

Second Editon

Contents

- Character Themes
- Vocabulary
- Introduction to Story
- Comprehension
- Discussion
- Sequencing
- Enrichment Ideas

Selections

Goals and Objectives

The *A Beka Book* Reading Program has two main goals: (1) to produce independent readers and writers and (2) to provide outstanding literary and character-building selections.

The teacher using the *A Beka Book* Reading Program should produce students who do the following:

1. Read with comprehension
2. Decode the written language easily
3. Read the Bible with understanding
4. Spell correctly
5. Appreciate and enjoy good literature
6. Acquire good character traits
7. Attain a large speaking and listening vocabulary
8. Recall facts easily
9. Write grammatically correct stories and poems
10. Read for knowledge and pleasure

Kind and Brave is an ideal book for beginning readers since it is correlated with the rules of phonics. Although students can now read many words without consciously sounding them out, they can tackle unfamiliar words with their decoding skills. The students are rapidly increasing their reading vocabulary and will be delighted with the stories and poems in *Kind and Brave*. The title of this book is justified as the children read about boys and girls who were kind and brave. They will delight in the animal fables which not only make enjoyable reading, but teach valuable character traits as well. First graders are developing a strong desire to know about their heritage and will enthusiastically read about the boyhoods of George Washington and Abraham Lincoln.

Important Techniques for the Reading Class ■■■■■■■■■■■■

Developing Reading Skills

Oral reading is a necessity for beginning readers. The student needs to hear himself sounding out the words, and the teacher needs to listen for correct decoding and expression. Oral reading gives the students supervised reading practice, develops their poise and delivery in reading, provides them an opportunity to improve their reading habits, and builds confidence. Silent reading will come naturally to the student who has been given thorough training in phonics and has had ample opportunity to practice his oral reading skills.

Before students begin reading, briefly review the phonics rules needed for the day's reading and have them read the practice word list at the end of the book that corresponds with the story to be read. Vocabulary practice is built into these lists, and the words used are designed to make reading of the passage easy and enjoyable. Words that need special attention are listed at the beginning of the selection to be read. Some of these are sight words, and you may need to help students pronounce them. Explain any unfamiliar words. Have the students say, spell, and say again the sight words.

Students enjoy testing their comprehension skill by reading and answering the comprehension questions provided in the text. Teachers can help students increase their comprehension by asking additional questions, both literal and interpretive. If a student continually gets the wrong answer, he needs to think more carefully about what he is reading. Discussing interesting words as well as the pictures in a selection may aid comprehension.

Your first graders will be pleased with how rapidly they master new reading material and glide from one reader to another. Through your skilled guidance, the children should look forward to reading class and seek extra reading activities. They will steadily grow in their love of reading.

Teachers appreciate a reading program that teaches children to read with comprehension and contains appropriate reading material. The suggestions presented in this Teacher Edition are designed to help you develop within your students the ability to read well, comprehend the written word, evaluate and analyze, and enjoy and appreciate good literature.

Evaluation of Reading

As students read aloud each day, encourage them to do their best, and point out their strong points. Also, correct any reading mistakes and have them reread if necessary. Plan to give each student one oral reading grade every week. Evaluate their reading as they read new material—not homework reading. Many students do better if evaluated during the morning reading session. To evaluate, observe the reading skills noted below, especially the skill presently being stressed. To evaluate comprehension, ask a question or two over the reading.

Look for the following skills in oral reading:

Accuracy: pronouncing words and reading sentences correctly.

Enunciation: saying the words clearly, not mumbling. Some will need to slow down for a while in order to accomplish this.

Smoothness: reading by phrases rather than word by word. No pauses unless called for by punctuation or context.

Alertness to punctuation: stopping at a period, pausing at a comma. The voice should drop at a period, rise at a question mark, and show excitement in an exclamatory sentence.

Expression: having good voice inflection to make the story interesting and realistic.

Comprehension: showing by expression and ability to answer questions a good understanding of the selection being read.

Volume: reading loudly enough to be heard clearly. Holding the book away from the face and keeping head up will help.

Speed: reading at a speed that allows accuracy, smoothness, and expression.

Poise: having confidence in reading and speaking before others.

Reading as an Integral Part of the Language Arts Program ▪▪▪▪▪▪▪▪▪▪

In the *A Beka Book* curriculum for Christian schools, reading is not an isolated subject but is an integral part of the Language Arts Program. The Language Arts Program consumes a large percentage of the school day since it consists of reading, phonics (in the early grades), grammar, spelling, vocabulary, penmanship, creative writing, story time, and library time.

Students taught by the *A Beka Book* Language Arts Program will easily sense the relationship of these subjects. In first grade, spelling is included in phonics class since most English words are spelled phonetically. Spelling lists in the early grades are grouped according to the rules of phonics. Students in reading class learn to read and spell the sight words simultaneously. Since spelling is incorporated into all areas, students taught by the *A Beka Book* Language Arts Program learn to spell many more words than those on the weekly spelling list.

The reading vocabulary in the *A Beka Book* Reading Program includes thousands of words. This is possible because students come to school with a large speaking vocabulary and when taught by the *A Beka Book* intensive phonics approach, they can easily read and understand them. The unfamiliar words are introduced by the teacher and serve to stretch the students' vocabularies. The *A Beka Book* Reading Program trains students to discover the meaning of unfamiliar words so they can read for understanding in all academic subjects.

Grammar is introduced early in the *A Beka Book* Language Arts Program. First graders begin their road to complete control of the English language by beginning each sentence with a capital letter and ending a telling sentence with a period. By observing written punctuation marks when reading, students not only can understand better what they are reading but can increase their awareness of the structure of language.

Students are given ample opportunity to write in the *A Beka Book* Program. Language, seatwork, history, science, reading, and special projects provide a variety of writing activities. Students are expected to use their spelling, grammar, vocabulary, and penmanship skills and to demonstrate their command of the language. Since the reading program supplies an abundance of good and varied reading material, students desire an opportunity to do their own writing. Students may want to create a character similar to one in a recent story, write a poem, describe a book they have read, or express in writing their thoughts about home, school, family, country, and God. The ability to read well naturally evolves into proficiency in other subject areas. The *A Beka Book* Reading Program facilitates the entire Language Arts Program.

A Balanced Reading Program

Reading is an exciting educational experience for children if they are given a variety of reading material. They should have delightful and thought-provoking poetry as well as prose. The prose should not include only their everyday world but should take them to faraway lands and times. Let them learn of Scotland or George Washington through the exciting pages of literature.

The *A Beka Book* Reading Program offers a well-rounded program in literature for children.

Fables. One of the goals of Christian teachers is to develop good character in their students. Offering a good sprinkling of fables will help the teacher attain this goal. A fable usually includes animals through which a moral lesson is taught. Children cherish animals and respond well to stories involving animals. The ant from "The Ant and the Dove" teaches the children gratitude, and the fox from "The Lion and the Bear" encourages harmony among classmates.

Folk Literature. Literature includes stories that have been passed down from one generation to the next. They were first told orally and then written down to guard against loss. "Mr. Rabbit and Tar Baby" is such a tale. Although the tale is unbelievable, it still makes an impression upon the reader. Other tales such as "Tommy and the Crows" are obviously untrue while clearly teaching a valuable lesson. Some tales are meant to amuse as they teach. "Goose-Goose and Pig-Pig" tickles the fancy as it guides students toward sharing.

Animal Tales. Some animal tales are fables, which give animals human qualities. Other animal stories present animals as animals. Children enjoy stories using pets or wild animals as main characters. All children will delight in Rover, the smart dog who saved two boys in a snowstorm, and the duck that would not give up.

Biographical Stories. Another aspect of children's literary heritage is biographical stories. Whether the stories feature events in the lives of famous Americans or Biblical heroes such as Moses or the everyday happenings of common folks, the children delight in these stories of yesteryear. Abraham Lincoln becomes a real person to the children as they read about his loving concern for his dog. Children experience a bond with the people of the past by reading stories that reveal the universality of human nature.

They identify with the characteristics which made these people worthy of recognition. Children, stimulated to read more about the character, expand their reading activities and experience the pleasure of erudition.

Scripture Reading. The primary goal of Christian education is to pass down Biblical knowledge and enable people to read the Bible for themselves. The Bible is the most important book for a Christian, since it contains the way of salvation and the plan for a Christian's life. Allowing children to read the Bible and the appropriately placed Scripture verses in the reading books develops ingrained Biblical principles. From time to time, remind the students that the Bible is different from anything else they will ever read because it is the Word of God and every word in it is true.

Poetry. A well-rounded literature program must include a good selection of poetry. The pleasing rhyme and rhythm of poetry make it a special delight to children. The same poem read several times in one sitting continues to give pleasure each time it is heard. Children want to practice their reading voices by reading the poem in a variety of arrangements. "Work and Play," "Two and One," and many other poems can easily be arranged into delightful choral readings.

Teaching Suggestions

Goose-Goose and Pig-Pig   pp. 4–7

- **Character Themes**

  Note: Discuss themes as stories are read orally. Encourage students to develop desirable character traits.

  Manners: Be a polite guest. Pig-Pig was greedy in the way he ate and in the amount he ate.

  Justice: Treat others as you want to be treated. In order to be treated fairly, Pig-Pig needed to learn to treat others fairly.

- **Vocabulary**

  Students should be able to sound out two-syllable words on p. 4 with little help. *Nothing* is partially a sight word. Have students say, spell, and say it again.

- **Introduction to Story**

  In this story Pig-Pig needs to learn a lesson about how to behave at his neighbor's house.

- **Comprehension**

  Note: Ask these questions as students read story orally. Students who fail to answer correctly may need to reread section.

  1. Did Pig-Pig have good manners? *no* p. 5 Why not? *He put his feet on the table, made noises with his mouth, upset his cup, and ate all the food.* p. 5

  2. Was Pig-Pig really sick when Goose-Goose came to visit? *No, he just didn't want to share.* p. 6

  3. Why wouldn't Goose-Goose share her dinner with Pig-Pig the second time he came to visit? *Because Pig-Pig had been selfish and unkind by not sharing with her.* p. 6

- **Discussion**

  As time allows, discuss proper table manners with students and have them tell what they would have done to help Pig-Pig.

Sunshine and Rain   pp. 8–10; Word List A, pp. 113–114

- **Character Theme**

  Contentment: Be thankful for what you have. Mark learned to enjoy the rain as well as the sunshine.

- **Vocabulary**

  Spend as much time as needed having students read word lists on pp. 113–114. Occasionally have them use each word in a pair in a sentence to show that they understand past tense. They should work for both speed and accuracy. Practice with selected lists of words will make reading of stories faster and more enjoyable. After this practice, students should be able to read their words on p. 8 with no trouble.

- **Introduction to Story**

  When you look outside and it's raining, are you happy, or do you wish for sunshine? Joy likes the rain; let's find out why.

- **Comprehension**

  Answers to "Do You Know Who?" p. 10

  Note: These questions should be discussed at end of oral reading. You may want to let students answer questions on paper occasionally.

  1. *God*
  2. *God*
  3. *God*
  4. *everyone*

  Additional questions

  1. What did Joy say the rain was like? *silver* p. 9
  2. Who complained about the rain? *Mark* p. 9
  3. What did the children do after they splashed in the puddles? *looked at books* p. 10
  4. Did Mark decide to enjoy the rain? *yes* p. 10

- **Discussion**

  Do you think Mark became a happier person by learning to be thankful even when he thought things were going wrong?

Ready to Go   pp. 11–15; Word List B, pp. 114–115

* **Character Theme**

  Cooperation: Working with others helps to get the work done more quickly. Because the boys help their parents do the work, they are able to visit their grandmother.

* **Vocabulary**

  As students read first group of words in Word List B, have them look for *o* that changes sound of *wh*. The *-ed* words are mixed up now, and students may need to read them more than once. Work for speed and accuracy. Choose one row of suffix words for students to use in sentences. As they read the "sound" sentences, mention that words have different meanings, depending on how they are used in a sentence. See how many special sounds students can find in the words on p. 11. *Laughed* is a sight word that they should learn to read and spell readily.

* **Introduction to Story**

  Have you ever been excited about visiting your grandparents? This story tells about how a family works together in order to visit their grandmother.

* **Comprehension**

  Answers to "Do You Know Who?" p. 15

  1. *Tom and Randy* p. 11
  2. *Daddy* p. 12
  3. *the boys* p. 12
  4. *Jean* pp. 12, 13
  5. *the boys and Jean* p. 13
  6. *everybody* p. 14
  7. *God*

  Additional questions

  1. Why did the boys say they could go to Grandmother's house? *no school the next day* p. 11
  2. Who was ready to go first? *Daddy* p. 13
  3. What did Jean wear? *her new white dress* p. 14
  4. What did the boys give Grandmother? *flowers* p. 14

- **Sequencing**

    Have students give story sequence. As they tell what happens next, write it on chalkboard (ckbd).

- **Discussion**

    Have students discuss ways they can help at home.

Mr. Rabbit and Tar Baby   pp. 16–20; Word List C, pp. 115–116

- **Character Theme**

    Self-control: When we become angry and strike out instead of controlling our temper, we get ourselves into all kinds of problems.

- **Vocabulary**

    As students read *tch* words on p. 115, remind them that this sound comes after a short vowel. See how fast they can recognize sight-word *laugh* on p. 16.

- **Introduction to Story**

    Do you know what tar is? Tar is a black, sticky material that is sometimes used to patch holes in roads. Let's read to find out what Mr. Fox made with some tar.

- **Comprehension**

    Answers to "Do You Know Why?" p. 20

    1. *to keep him out of his garden* p. 17

    2. *to watch Mr. Rabbit without being seen* pp. 17, 18

    3. *He thought Tar Baby was stuck up.* p. 18

    4. *Tar is sticky.*

    Additional questions

    1. What did Mr. Fox use to make the Tar Baby? *sticks and tar* p. 17 Explain that they may have seen tar being used to fill holes in roads during the summertime or to put roofing materials on houses.

    2. Where did Mr. Fox hide? *in the corn patch* p. 18

    3. Why didn't Tar Baby say anything? *because he wasn't a real person, and so he couldn't talk* p. 18

4. Do you think Mr. Rabbit did right to hit the Tar Baby? *no*

5. Do you think Mr. Rabbit is going to get away? *Answers vary.*

• Discussion

Discuss importance of self-control. Tell students that they will read end of story in next selection.

Mr. Rabbit Gets Away   pp. 21–25; Word List D, p. 116

• Vocabulary

Read section 1 of Word List D once for pronunciation and then again for speed. Have someone use *duet* and *poet* in sentences. Talk about the word *create* and have students read Bible verse in unison. Read section 2 and then ask what kind of word *won't* is on p. 21 (*a contraction*).

• Introduction to Story

Mr. Rabbit is really stuck up, isn't he? Do you think he will ever get away from Mr. Fox? Let's read and find out.

• Comprehension

Answers to "Do You Know?" p. 25

1. *"How do you do, Mr. Rabbit? You look stuck up this morning."* p. 22

2. *because he really wanted Mr. Fox to throw him there* p. 24

3. *The briers tore off the tar.* p. 24

Additional questions

1. What did Mr. Fox do when he saw Mr. Rabbit stuck to the Tar Baby? *laughed* p. 21

2. What did Mr. Fox plan to do to Mr. Rabbit? *eat him for supper* p. 22

3. Why did Mr. Rabbit ask Mr. Fox not to throw him into the brier patch? *because that was just where Mr. Rabbit wanted to be, and he knew that Mr. Fox was so mean he would do the very thing Mr. Rabbit asked him not to do* p. 24

4. How do you think Mr. Fox felt when Mr. Rabbit said, "Thanks, Mr. Fox"? *probably very foolish*

- **Sequencing**

     Use "Mr. Rabbit and Tar Baby," pp. 16–20 and "Mr. Rabbit Gets Away," pp. 21–25. Following list of events is from stories listed above. Write list on ckbd and challenge students to identify them in order in which they happened.

     _4_ Mr. Rabbit asks not to be thrown into the brier patch. pp. 22, 23, 24

     _1_ Mr. Rabbit eats the good things in Mr. Fox's garden. p. 17

     _5_ Mr. Fox throws Mr. Rabbit into the brier patch. p. 24

     _3_ Mr. Rabbit gets "stuck up" in the Tar Baby. pp. 19, 20, 21, 22

     _2_ Mr. Fox makes a Tar Baby. p. 17

     (Proper order and page numbers are included for the teacher's information.)

Grandmother's Path   pp. 26–32; Word List E, p. 117

- **Character Themes**

     Industry: A job worth doing is worth doing well. Bob thought of a good way to help his grandmother. He did his job well.

     Perseverance: Once a project is begun, it is important to finish it. Even though his work took a long time, Bob did not quit.

- **Vocabulary**

     Have students read Word List E vertically and then horizontally. Individuals should read Bible verses. Point out two pronunciations for *lives* on p. 26.

- **Introduction to Story**

     When you have a hard job to do, the best way to get it done is one step at a time. The boy in this story found this was true. He proves it by the way he does his job.

- **Comprehension**

     1. Who lived next door to Grandmother? *Bob and Becky* p. 26

     2. Did Bob love his grandmother? *yes* How can you tell? *He was concerned about her and wanted to make sure it would be easy for her to come and see them.* p. 28

3. What three people did Bob talk to while he was working? *milkman* p. 29, *paper boy* p. 30, *mailman* p. 31

4. How did Bob clear the path? *a little at a time* p. 32

- **Discussion**

    1. Challenge students with the *Something to Do* suggestions on p. 32.

    2. Have students read and discuss "The Bible Says," p. 33.

    3. Have students read poem "Work and Play," p. 33 and tell why they think Bob would like that poem.

Why Jimmy Did His Work   pp. 34–40;

Word List F, p. 117

- **Character Theme**

    Responsibility: Realize that you need to be responsible to do your work. Do not be lazy. Jimmy found that he enjoyed his work.

- **Vocabulary**

    Before students read sec. 1 of Word List F, remind them that **mb in lamb** can make the vowel before it either long or short. Have students make sentences like ones on p. 118 for word *play.*

- **Comprehension**

    Answers to "Do You Know?" p. 40

    1. *No; animals don't really talk.* pp. 36, 37, 38

    2. *He wanted to play instead.* p. 35

    3. *He did not want to be like the pigs.* p. 39

    Additional questions

    1. When should we play? *after the work is done* p. 35

    2. What did Jimmy learn about work? *It is fun.* p. 39

- **Discussion**

    1. Do you think Jimmy lived in the city or the country? *He must live in the country, on a farm with sheep, chickens, and pigs.*

18

2. Do you think playing and eating are better than working? (You could bring out that if everyone felt this were true, there would be nobody to grow and prepare our food or even to make the toys we like to play with.)

- **Enrichment Idea**

    Read and discuss poems on pp. 40 and 41.

Dotty and Spotty   pp. 42–46; Word List G, p. 118

- **Character Themes**

    Kindness: Be kind to others. Dotty and Spotty learned to be kind. A willingness to share and think of others before ourselves is something even first graders can do.

    Justice: Selfishness brings unhappiness. Dotty and Spotty received a punishment for their selfishness.

- **Vocabulary**

    Read Word List G.

- **Introduction to Story**

    If there is only one cookie left in the cookie jar, are you willing to let your sister or brother have it or do you want it for yourself? Let's find out what happens to two kittens who want the same mouse.

- **Comprehension**

    Answers to "Think About It," p. 46

    1. *He was upset.* p. 44
    2. *He wanted the mouse.* p. 44
    3. *because they were fighting* p. 45
    4. *share and be kind* p. 46
    5. *because they had learned to share and be kind to each other* pp. 45, 46

- **Discussion**

    Read and discuss "The Bible Says," "A Good Rule," and "Do Good," p. 47. Would Dotty and Spotty have been spared some discomfort if they had heard these words before they saw mouse?

A Brave Dog   pp. 48–52; Word List H, p. 118

- **Character Themes**

    Common Sense: Before doing something we should think about the consequences of our actions. If Ronny and Jack had thought about what could happen to them, they would have started home when the first snowflakes began to fall.

    Thankfulness: If we are truly thankful, we will show it by our actions. Ronny and Jack were very glad that Rover helped them home. They showed him their gratefulness by giving him a big dinner.

- **Vocabulary**

    In sec. 1 of Word List H, have students read root word and entire word. In sec. 2, have students read as quickly as they can.

- **Introduction to Story**

    This story shows what could happen when we don't think ahead. Think about what Ronny and Jack should have done while we read the story.

- **Comprehension**

    Answers to "Think About It," p.52

    1. *They were lost in a snowstorm.* p. 50

    2. *Rover* pp. 50, 51 *He led them home.* p. 52

    3. *Answers vary.*

    4. *They fed him a big dinner before they ate.* p. 52

- **Discussion**

    What should Kenny and Jack have done?

- **Enrichment Idea**

    Have students read the poem on page 53.

- **Sequencing**

    Following list of events is from story. Write list on ckbd and challenge students to identify them in order in which they happened.

Two Dogs   pp. 54–57; Word List I, p. 119

- ## Character Theme

  Kindness: Treat your pets with kindness and care for them properly. Jip was not cared for by his master, and Jip did not love him.

- ## Vocabulary

  Have students work for speed with Word List I.

- ## Introduction to Story

  Do you have a pet? Do you treat it kindly? Which dog in this story would be yours?

- ## Comprehension

  Answers to "Something to Talk About," p. 57

  1. *Jack, because his master loved and cared for him* pp. 55, 56

  2. *Answers vary.*

  3. *Answers vary.*

  Additional questions

  1. How could a person tell by looking at Jip that he was cared for poorly? *He was dirty and thin.*

  2. Why was Jip afraid of his master? *He was cross.*

  3. Identify the dogs on page 57. *top—Jack; bottom—Jip*

- ## Enrichment Idea

  Have students write a story as though their pet is describing what kind of master they are.

The Wind and the Duck
pp. 58–61;
Word List J, pp. 119–120

- **Character Theme**

  Persistence: Don't give up. The duck did not give up even though the North Wind tried and tried to stop him.

- **Vocabulary**

  Word List J. Students may need time to figure out some of words and phrases in sec. 1.

- **Introduction to Story**

  When our job is difficult, it is important to stick with it. This story is about a duck that kept doing his work even when the wind tried to stop him.

- **Comprehension**

  Answers to "Do You Know?" p. 61

  1. *to find fish to eat* p. 59

  2. *no* p. 59

  3. *He probably would have starved to death.*

  4. *He never gave up.* pp. 60, 61

The Ant and the Dove
pp. 62–65; Word List K, p. 120

- **Character Themes**

  Service: Be willing to help someone else because you may need their help someday.

  Thoughtfulness: Helping others is a good way to find happiness.

- **Vocabulary**

  After students read definitions in Word List K, have them think of sentences for defined words.

- **Introduction to Story**

  Do you have a good friend? The way to have friends is to be a friend and help others.

22

- **Comprehension**
  Answers to "Think About It," p.65
    1. *She couldn't get out of the brook.* p. 63
    2. *a dove* p. 63 *by dropping a leaf to her* p. 63
    3. *A hunter was going to shoot him.* p. 64
    4. *the ant* p. 64 *She bit the hunter's foot and stopped him from shooting.* p. 64
    5. *Answers vary.*
    6. *Be kind. Be helpful. Be thankful.*

- **Discussion**
    1. Discuss with students saying "Do unto others as you would have them do unto you."
    2. Discuss meaning of Proverbs 18:24.

- **Enrichment Idea**
    Have students give a list of ways they can be a friend to their classmates. Have a few students share their lists with class.

The Lion and the Bear   pp. 66–68

- **Character Theme**
    Selflessness: Be willing to share. The lion and the bear were selfish. Each wanted the fawn for himself.

- **Introduction to Story**
    How often do you argue over who will be first or who has more? The lion and the bear in the story today have a silly quarrel which brings them unhappiness.

- **Comprehension**
  Answers to "Do You Know?" p. 68
    1. *a fight* p. 66
    2. *a fawn* p. 67
    3. *Neither was right.*
    4. *They could have shared.*
    5. *It was both their faults.*

• Enrichment Ideas

1. Have students write another ending to story to show how lion and bear should have acted toward each other.

2. Have students read poem "Two and One," p. 69, as a choral reading.

Two and One

Boys: I have two ears and only one mouth;
The reason, I think, is clear:
All: It teaches me that it will not do
To talk about all I hear.

Girls: I have two eyes and only one mouth;
The reason of this must be,
All: That I should learn it will not do
To talk about all I see.

Boys: I have two hands and only one mouth;
And it is worth repeating:
All: The two are for work that I need to do—
The one is for eating.

The Foolish Weather Vane   pp. 70–75;
Word List L, p. 121

• Character Themes

Honesty: Always tell the truth. The weather vane lied to the fishermen.

Service: Help others without being proud of the help you give. The weather vane was a helper for many people until he decided to do wrong because of his pride.

• Vocabulary

Word List L

• Introduction to Story

What does it mean to be foolish? Let's read and see why this weather vane is called "foolish."

- **Comprehension**

  ### Answers to "Do You Know?" p. 75

  1. *a piece of metal that tells which direction the wind is blowing* p. 70
  2. *because the man looked to him for direction* pp. 71, 72
  3. *to do as he wanted rather than obeying the wind* p. 74
  4. *no* pp. 72, 73 *no* p. 73
  5. *because he could not be trusted* p. 74
  6. *always*

- **Discussion**

  1. Discuss with students how being dishonest causes others not to trust them, even when they tell truth. You might want to read them story about little boy who cried "wolf."
  2. Read and discuss "The Bible Says," p. 75.
  3. Read and discuss "Who Has Seen the Wind?" p. 75.

Funny Bunny   pp. 76–83; Word List M, p. 122

- **Character Themes**

  Common Sense: Don't believe everything you hear. The lion used his common sense and did not believe the animals' story.

  Trust: Students can be wise like the lion if they think before they act. Don't worry about what might happen. Trust God to take care of you. The bunny's troubles began when he began to worry about what might happen.

- **Vocabulary**

  Some words in Word Practice M may require some thought. Have students read words as quickly as they can. Some students may need help with the following words in story:

coconut	mistake	beasts
monkeys	roared	

- **Introduction to Story**

    Funny Bunny has a scary thought and jumps to the wrong conclusion about a noise he hears. He doesn't stop to use his common sense. As we read the story, see how many of the animals don't use their common sense.

- **Comprehension**

    Answers to "Think!" p. 83

    1. *What if the world should break up?* pp. 77, 83 *No. We should not worry about things that may never happen.*

    2. *a coconut* p. 77 *The earth was breaking up.* p. 77

    3. *Looked to see what had really happened*

    4. *They listened to Funny Bunny rather than checking things out for themselves.*

    5. *the lion, the King of Beasts* p. 82 *He checked things out and helped Funny Bunny and the other animals see that there was nothing to be afraid of.*

- **Discussion**

    Have students give examples of when they could use good judgment. Some answers may be—when crossing street, playing a game, or spending money.

Tommy and the Crows   pp. 84–91; Word List N, p. 123

- **Character Theme**

    Duty: Do right because it is right to do right. It was Tommy's duty to go to school.

- **Vocabulary**

    Word List N

- **Introduction to Story**

    A lazy boy refuses to go to school but is taught a valuable lesson by some crows.

- **Comprehension**

    Answers to "Do You Know?" p. 91

    1. *He wanted to play.* p. 85 *no* pp. 86, 87

2. *make nests,* pp. 86, 87 *grow coats,* p. 88, and *get food for themselves,* p. 90

3. *God taught them.*

4. *schools*

5. *Answers vary.*

George Washington pp. 92–94; Word List O, pp. 123–124

• Character Themes

Patriotism: Love your country. George Washington became a soldier to help America become a free nation.

Duty: It is our duty to do our best. George Washington tried each day to do his best.

• Vocabulary

Word List O. Some students may need help with words on p. 92.

• Introduction to Story

George Washington was the first President of our country. He learned many things as a boy that helped him when he grew up. Let's find out what kind of person George Washington was.

• Comprehension

1. What did George like to play? *soldier* p. 93

2. What kind of game were the boys playing when George drilled them? *Answers may vary. (soldier, marching, etc.)* p. 93

3. Who was his best teacher? *his mother* p. 93

4. What kind of country did George Washington help America become? *free* p. 94

5. What important lesson can we learn from George Washington? *to do our best every day* p. 94

Lincoln and His Dog   pp. 95–98; Word List P, p. 124

- ## Character Theme

    Compassion: Be willing to help others who are weaker than you. Lincoln showed love and care for his dog. We can learn to care about others as he cared for his dog.

- ## Vocabulary

    Word List P

- ## Introduction to Story

    Abraham Lincoln was a famous President of the United States. He loved and cared for people. His kindness started when he was just a boy. As we read, notice how he cares for a little dog.

- ## Comprehension

    1. Was Abraham Lincoln's family rich? *no* p. 95
    2. At what season of the year did this story take place? *winter*
    3. What kind of animal pulled their wagon? *oxen* p. 96
    4. What kind of master was Abe to his dog? *kind* p. 98
    5. How can you tell? *He waded in the icy water to get him.* p. 98

- ## Discussion

    How was moving from one home to another different for Abe Lincoln's family than it is for a family today?

- ## Enrichment Ideas

    Have students pretend they are Abraham Lincoln's dog and write their master a thank-you letter.

The Story of Moses   pp. 99–112; Word List Q, p. 125

- ## Character Themes

    Courage: God will help you to do what must be done. Moses' parents showed courage in keeping their baby. Miriam

28

showed courage in watching the basket and speaking to the princess.

Family: Cooperate and help your family. The family worked together to care for their baby.

• Vocabulary

Word List Q. Students may need help with the words on p. 99.

• Introduction to Story

Because today's story is from the Bible, it is true. Wicked Pharaoh, the ruler of Egypt, ordered all the Hebrew boy babies to be killed. But God had other plans for baby Moses.

• Comprehension

1. What country did Pharaoh rule? *Egypt* p. 100

2. What did Moses' mother use to make the basket? *bulrushes and tar* p. 104

3. Who watched Moses from the bulrushes? *Miriam* p. 107

4. Who found Moses in the basket? *the princess* p. 109

5. Did it just happen that the princess came to the river while Moses and Miriam were there? *No. God planned it and was watching and caring for them.*

6. Who was appointed to care for Baby Moses? *his mother* p. 111

7. What did Moses say when he became a leader of his people? *God will help me and take care of me.* p. 112

• Sequencing

Challenge students to identify order in which these events happened.

_4_ Moses is found by the princess. p. 109

_3_ Moses' mother makes a basket. p. 104

_1_ Pharaoh wants all boy babies thrown into the river. p. 100

_5_ Moses becomes a leader of his people. p. 112

_2_ Miriam and Aaron help their mother. p. 103

Kind and Brave

by
Laurel Hicks

illustrated by
Walter Kerr

A Beka Book®
A MINISTRY OF
PENSACOLA CHRISTIAN COLLEGE
PENSACOLA, FLORIDA 32523-9160

To the Teacher

Children are eagerly searching for a workable sense of values. They need to see in the lives of great people, common people, and children like themselves, the unchanging values of the ages lived out. They need reading material that will give them ideals to reach for and examples to follow.

The stories in *Kind and Brave* have been selected from the readers of America's past and have been edited, modernized, and classroom-tested for student appeal and readability. These values are taught throughout the book— honesty, integrity, courage, faith, kindness, forgiveness, industry, unselfishness, patriotism, and respect for authority. Thought questions at the end of the stories greatly aid in the understanding and appreciation of the selections. *Kind and Brave* should be read after students have mastered Phonics Charts 1–9 and while they are learning charts 10–11.

Grateful acknowledgment is extended to Mr. Daniel LaRue for permission to reprint "Goose-Goose and Pig-Pig," and "Dotty and Spotty," from *The F-U-N Book,* by Mabel Guinnip LaRue, copyright 1923, 1930 by the Macmillan Company, copyright 1958 by Mabel Guinnip LaRue.

Third Editon

Copyright © 1995, 1986, 1973 Pensacola Christian College
All rights reserved. Printed in U.S.A. 2001 C01

Contents

Words to Watch For

dinner   garden   upset
hungry   table   nothing

Goose-Goose
and
Pig-Pig

One day Pig-Pig went to see Goose-Goose.

Pig-Pig said, "I will come to eat with you, Goose-Goose. Get a good dinner. I am hungry. I can eat all day."

"I will," said Goose-Goose. "I will cook all I have in the house and all I have in the garden." And she did.

When Pig-Pig came to the table, he upset his cup with his nose. He put his feet on the table. He made a noise with his mouth. And he ate the dinner all up. Goose-Goose had nothing.

The next day, Goose-Goose went to see Pig-Pig. Pig-Pig saw her come down the road, and he ran and got into bed.

When Goose-Goose came to the door, Pig-Pig said, "I cannot get dinner for you today, Goose-Goose. I am sick. I must stay in bed."

So Goose-Goose went back home.

The next day, Goose-Goose was eating her dinner. Pig-Pig came to the door. He said, "I have come again, Goose-Goose, to eat with you."

But Goose-Goose said, "No, no, Pig-Pig, no, no. You were sick when I came to see you. You look sick today. Go back to bed."

Pig-Pig was cross. He said, "Wee, wee, wee," all the way home.

Words to Watch For

rained   liked   puddles

raining   silver   splashed

Sunshine and Rain

One day it rained and rained.

Joy liked the rain. She liked to splash in the puddles. She liked to get her boots wet.

"The rain is like silver," said Joy. "Look at me splashing in the silver."

"I don't want to splash," said Mark. "I want to play in the sun and have some fun. When will it stop raining, Mother?"

"I know!" said Joy. "It will stop raining when it's time to stop raining. Come on, Mark. Splash with me in the puddles. Then we can look at some books. The rain is helping the plants to grow."

"Oh, all right," said Mark. "I may as well play with you."

Joy and Mark splashed in the puddles, and then they looked at some books.

"This is fun," said Mark. "I like the rain. I like to splash in puddles, and I like to look at books. Thank you, God, for sending the rain. Thank you for helping the plants to grow."

Do You Know Who?

1. Who made the sun?
2. Who made the stars?
3. Who made the rain?
4. Who should say "Thank You"?

Ready to Go

Words to Watch For

visit	when	could
flowers	while	ready
school	laughed	tomorrow

One day Tom and Randy came running home from school.

Tom said, "Mother, Mother! There's no school tomorrow. Why don't we go to Grandmother's house? Please let us go."

Little Jean was in the house. She liked to visit Grandmother.

Daddy was afraid they could not go. He said it would be fun, but he was afraid they could not get ready in time.

"We must put away our play things," he said. "We must water the flowers before we go."

"But we could help!" the boys cried.

Tom said, "I will put away the play things while Randy waters the flowers. It will all be done in no time."

How the boys did work! It was fun to watch them.

Soon everything was done. Tom put away the play things. Randy gave the flowers some water. He picked some

for Grandmother, too, and Jean helped
him.

Daddy had gone into the house to
get dressed. When Mother came out,
she was surprised to see that the
work was all done.

"Everything is done, Mother," said
Tom. "We had fun, too. See the
flowers that Jean picked!"

Daddy was all dressed up and
waiting in the car. "I am ready to
go," he said. "Am I going alone, or is
someone going with me?"

How Tom laughed at that!

Daddy got out and put the flowers
into the car. Then he looked the car
over. He wanted everything to be
right. He put the bags in. He was
ready to go.

"Where is Mother?" he asked.

"She is coming," said Tom.

Just then little Jean and Mother came out. Jean had on her new white dress. She looked so pretty! Mother had on her new yellow dress. Tom and Randy were both ready to go, so off they all went to Grandmother's farm.

Grandmother came out to hug the children. She was glad to see them.

She was so pleased when Tom and Randy gave her the flowers! "Oh, thank you!" she said again and again. "What pretty flowers! But how did Mother get ready so soon?"

Then she looked at the boys. "I think I know," she said. "I think I know!"

Do You Know Who?

1. Who wanted to go to Grandmother's house?
2. Who was afraid they could not get ready?
3. Who said that they would help?
4. Who helped Randy pick the flowers?
5. Who had fun?
6. Who was happy?
7. Who wants us to always do our best?

Words to Watch For

watch   catch   laugh   other

watched   patch   tar   pulled

Mr. Rabbit
and
Tar Baby

Once upon a time Mr. Fox had a garden. He had good things to eat in his garden.

Now, Mr. Rabbit liked good things to eat, so he went into Mr. Fox's garden day after day.

Each day, Mr. Fox watched Mr. Rabbit eating in his garden. He said to himself, "I will catch that rabbit and make him stay out of my garden."

Mr. Fox made a Tar Baby out of some sticks and some dark, sticky tar. He put Tar Baby up in the garden.

Then Mr. Fox said to himself, "I will hide in the corn patch and see how Mr. Rabbit likes the Tar Baby."

Mr. Rabbit hopped into the garden to get something good to eat. Mr. Fox watched him, keeping very still.

When Mr. Rabbit saw Tar Baby, he said, "Good morning." But Tar Baby said nothing.

Mr. Rabbit said, "How are you this morning?" But Tar Baby said nothing.

Then Mr. Rabbit called out, "How are you this morning? Can't you hear?" But Tar Baby said nothing.

Mr. Rabbit said, "You are stuck up, you are! I am going to hit you."

Mr. Fox was laughing to himself, keeping very still all the while.

Mr. Rabbit hit Tar Baby with his hand, and his hand stuck fast. He pulled and pulled, but he could not get his hand away.

Mr. Rabbit called out, "If you don't let me go, I'll hit you with my other hand." But Tar Baby did not let him go.

Mr. Rabbit hit Tar Baby with his other hand, and it stuck fast, too.

Then Mr. Rabbit called out, "If you don't let me go, I'll kick you." But Tar Baby did not let him go.

Mr. Fox laughed to himself, but he was keeping very still.

Mr. Rabbit kicked Tar Baby with one foot, and his foot stuck fast. He pulled and pulled, but he could not get away.

Do You Know Why?

1. Why did Mr. Fox want to catch Mr. Rabbit?
2. Why did Mr. Fox hide in the corn patch?
3. Why did Mr. Rabbit hit Tar Baby?
4. Why didn't Tar Baby let Mr. Rabbit go?

Mr. Rabbit Gets Away

Words to Watch For

head   won't   brier   river

A **brier** is a sticker.

Then Mr. Rabbit called out, "If you don't let me go, I'll kick you with my other foot." But Tar Baby did not let him go.

Mr. Fox was watching and laughing to himself.

Then Mr. Rabbit called out, "Let me go, or I'll hit you with my head." But Tar Baby said nothing and did not let him go.

Mr. Rabbit hit Tar Baby with his head, and it stuck fast, too.

Then Mr. Fox laughed and came out of the corn patch. He said, "How do you do, Mr. Rabbit? You look stuck up this morning." Mr. Fox laughed till he could laugh no more.

"Please let me go, Mr. Fox," said Mr. Rabbit. "I won't come here again."

But Mr. Fox began to lay some dry wood around Tar Baby and Mr. Rabbit. "I got you this time," he said.

"Burn me if you want to," said Mr. Rabbit, "but don't throw me into the brier patch. Please don't throw me into the briers."

"I'll throw you into the river. That's what I'll do," grinned Mr. Fox.

"All right, Mr. Fox. Throw me into the river, just as deep as you please.

But don't, please don't throw me into the brier patch."

"I think I'll hang you," said Mr. Fox, and his grin was not good to see.

"Hang me, Mr. Fox," said Mr. Rabbit. "Hang me just as high as you can. But don't, please don't throw me into the brier patch."

Old Mr. Fox looked at him, and now he was not grinning a bit. "Into the briers you go!" he said. And with that, he tossed Mr. Rabbit right into the brier patch.

There was a lot of noise. The briers were helping Mr. Rabbit to get away from the Tar Baby. And there, away up on the hill, stood Mr. Rabbit. He called out: "Thanks, Mr. Fox. My home is in the briers. That's where I live."

And away he went.

Do You Know?

1. What did Mr. Fox say when he came out of the corn patch?
2. Why did Mr. Rabbit say, "Don't throw me into the brier patch?"
3. How did Mr. Rabbit get away?

Words to Watch For

clear	earth	love	breakfast
hear	early	shovel	lives

Grandmother's Path

Grandmother lives next door to Bob and Becky. There is a little path from her house to the children's home.

Every day Grandmother goes along this little path to see Bob and Becky and Baby. This is why they call it Grandmother's path.

One night it snowed. Big snow-flakes fell on the tops of the roofs and on the trees. They fell in the yard and on Grandmother's path.

When morning came, the whole earth seemed white with snow.

Bob woke up early and sat up. Then he jumped out of bed and ran to the window.

When he looked out, the happy boy shouted, "It's snowing! It's snowing!"

He could hear Mother fixing break-fast.

He called out, "Look, Mother! Grandmother's path is all white with snow. She can't come over the path this morning to see us. May I clear it for her?"

"Making a path is hard work, but you may try, Bob," said Mother.

After breakfast, Bob put on his coat, his scarf, and his earmuffs. Then he put on his boots.

He got Father's snow shovel and went to work. "I'll clear the path for Grandmother," he said.

Bob cleared the path a little way. Then he stopped to rest. Soon he began working again.

"Mother is right," said Bob. "Making a path is hard work."

When the milkman came with the milk, he watched Bob for a while.

Then the milkman said,

"To make a path, my little man,
    You're working hard today;
Little by little, step by step,
    You'll clear the snow away."

"Yes," said Bob, "I'm making a path for Grandmother."

Bob went on clearing the path.

Soon the paper boy came with Father's newspaper. He watched Bob for a while.

Then the paper boy said,

"To make a path, my little man,
    You're working hard today;
Little by little, step by step,
    You'll clear the snow away."

"Yes," said Bob, "I'm making a path for Grandmother."

Bob went on clearing the path.

The mailman came with letters. He watched Bob for a while.

Then the mailman said,

> "To make a path, my little man,
>   You're working hard today;
> Little by little, step by step,
>   You'll clear the snow away."

"Yes," said Bob, "I'm making a path for Grandmother."

Bob cleared the path to Grandmother's house. Then he looked up, and there stood Grandmother in the door.

"Grandmother," called out Bob. "I have made a path for you."

"Well, well," said Grandmother. "And a fine path it is. How did you do such a hard job as that?"

Then Bob said,

"Because I love you, Grandma, dear,
 I worked so hard today.
Little by little, step by step,
 I cleared the snow away."

———— Something to Do ————

Can you think of something hard that you can do for someone you love? What will be the best way to get the job done? Do not tell anyone what you will do. Let it be a surprise. Think of what you will do, and then do it, "little by little, step by step." Here are some jobs that you may want to choose from:

1. Wash the dishes for Mother.
2. Rake the leaves for Father.
3. Fix a toy for your little brother or sister.
4. Make something for a friend.

The Bible Says

"And Jacob served seven years for Rachel; and they seemed unto him but a few days, for the love he had to her."

–Genesis 29:20

Work and Play

Work while you work;
Play while you play.
That is the way
To be happy each day.

All that you do,
Do with your might.
Things done in part
Are never done right.

–M. A. Stodart

Words to Watch For

old	holding	any
told	washing	would

Why Jimmy Did His Work

Jimmy was picking apples. Father had told him to fill a basket, but Jimmy did not feel like working.

"I don't want to pick these old apples," Jimmy said. "I just want to play. I'll go get someone to play with me."

He put his basket under the tree and ran to Sandy's house.

"Sandy! Sandy!" he called. "Will you come out and play with me?"

But Sandy was helping Mother. She was holding the baby. "After I do my work, I may play," she said. "Don't you have any work to do?"

Jimmy would not tell her. He ran back to his house.

"I'll get Kitty to play with me," Jimmy said.

But Kitty was washing her little kitten.

"Oh, no!" she said. "After I do my work, I may play. Don't you have any work to do?"

But Jimmy would not tell her. He ran down the road.

"I'll get my dog to play with me," he said.

"Come, Tip! Come, Tip! Come and play with me!" he called.

"Oh, no!" Tip said. "I must watch these sheep. Would you have me run away from the sheep? After I do my work, I may play. Don't you have any work to do?"

But Jimmy would not tell him. He went away.

Jimmy came to Old Hen and her baby chicks.

"Will you play with me, Old Hen?" Jimmy called. "Sandy and Tip and Kitty are working, but I want to play."

Old Hen did not say a word. She was working too fast. How her feet did go!

"Cluck, cluck, scratch, scratch," she said to her chicks. Then she made the sand fly.

She looked up at Jimmy. "This is the way I work. I do not play. Don't you have any work to do?"

Jimmy would not tell her. He went away.

Jimmy walked on and came to some pigs.

"Oink, oink," called the pigs. "We hear you don't like to work; and we don't like to work. You will not see us work. We like to eat and eat and eat. Playing and eating are better than working."

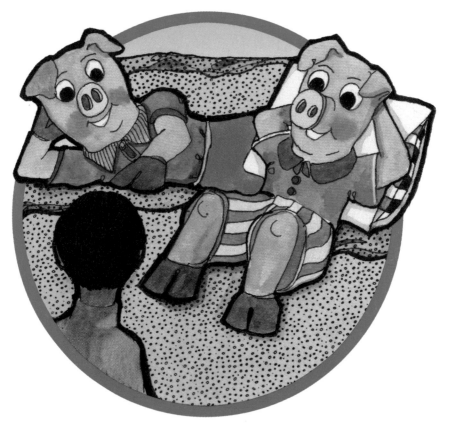

Jimmy was looking at the pigs. He put on his thinking cap.

Here is what Jimmy was thinking:

"Sandy is working. She is helping her mother."

"Kitty is working. She is washing her kittens."

"Tip is looking after the sheep. Old Hen is feeding her chicks."

"The pigs are not working. They just eat and eat. I do not want to be like pigs."

Then he said, "Father told me to work, and that's what I'll do!"

So he ran back to the apple tree and began picking up apples and putting them into the basket. He soon filled the basket with the red apples.

"Why, this is fun!" said Jimmy.

Do You Know?

1. Is this a true story?
   How can you tell?
2. Why didn't Jimmy want to work?
3. Why did Jimmy start working?

I'm a little teapot,
   Short and stout.
Here is my handle,
   Here is my spout.
When I get all steamed up,
   Then I shout,
Just tip me over and pour me out!

Jack Sprat could eat no fat;
   His wife could eat no lean.
And so between them both, you see,
   They licked the platter clean.

Four ducks on a pond,
A grass-bank beyond,
A blue sky of spring,
White clouds on the wing—

What a little thing
To remember for years!
To remember with tears!
                    –*William Allingham*

Words to Watch For

mew	cold	scratch	whacked
blew	fire	swept	opened
flew	whack	crept	another

Dotty and Spotty

Once upon a time there were two little kittens.

One was all white with one black spot. Her name was Spotty.

One was all black with one white dot. Her name was Dotty.

One cold night, Dotty and Spotty sat by the fire. Mother Gray Cat came into the room. She had a mouse.

Up jumped Dotty, and up jumped Spotty.

"Mew, mew, Mother," said Dotty. "Please give that mouse to me."

"No, no, Mother," said Spotty. "I want that mouse."

Then Dotty said, "You shall not have that mouse, Spotty. It is my mouse."

And Spotty said, "I will have the mouse. Ffft! Ffft!"

"We shall see about that," said Dotty, and Dotty gave Spotty a whack with her paw.

Then those two little kittens began to fight. They whacked and they spit. They scratched and they bit.

Soon an old lady ran into the room. She had a broom. She opened the door, and she swept Dotty and Spotty right out of the room.

It was a cold night. The wind blew, and the snow flew. Dotty and Spotty sat down by the door. Oh, how they did cry!

After a while, the old lady opened the door to shake her tablecloth.

Dotty and Spotty crept into the house and under the stove. Mother Gray Cat was there. She said, "Here is the mouse, kittens."

"Give it to Dotty," said Spotty.

"No, no," said Dotty. "Give it to Spotty."

"Now you are good kittens," said Mother Gray Cat. "I will go to the barn and catch another mouse right away."

Think About It

1. Why did Spotty say "Ffft! Ffft!"?
2. Why did Dotty hit Spotty?
3. Why did the old lady sweep the kittens out of the room?
4. What did Dotty and Spotty learn to do?
5. Why did Mother Gray Cat say, "Now you are good kittens"?

The Bible Says

"And be ye kind one to another."
                              –*Ephesians 4:32*

A Good Rule

Be to others kind and true
As you'd have others be to you.

Do Good

Do all the good you can
In all the ways you can
To all the people you can
As long as ever you can.

–John Wesley

47

Words to Watch For

faster   snowflake
loudly   together

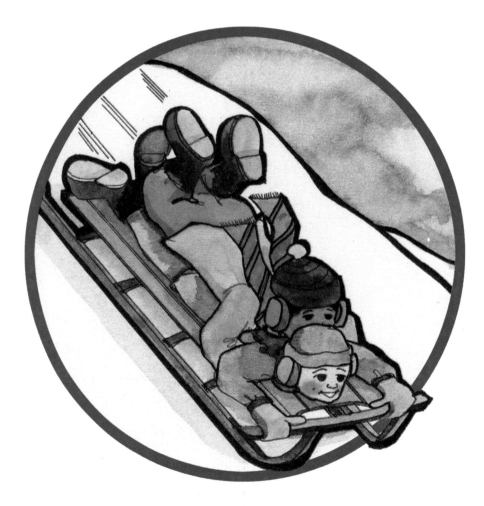

A Brave Dog

"Come on, Ronny," called Jack to his best friend. "Today will be a fine day to try out the long hill over in the woods."

"Think it will snow?" asked Ronny. "It looks like it."

"Oh, no," said Jack. "And we won't stay long. We'll just take a few slides and then come home. It's not far."

But Jack was not right this time. It was a long walk to the hill. Before they had made a good track on the hill, a snowflake fell on Ronny's nose.

But the hill was so long and the slide was so fine that the boys could not stop.

Then all at once a storm, a big storm, was upon them.

The boys knew it was a bad snow storm, so they started off for home at once.

"It's this way," called Ronny.

"No, it's this way," called Jack.

The wind was blowing. The snow was coming down faster and faster. They could not see which way to go.

The two boys kept together, but they soon began to be afraid. They knew they could never find their way home in such a storm.

Now Rover, Jack's dog, had run on. Soon he came running back, barking loudly. Then he ran off again. He was out of sight very soon. Back he came again, barking more loudly than ever.

"I think he wants us to follow him," said Ronny. Then the boys tried to follow him. But they could not keep up with him for the wind and snow. They stopped.

Back came Rover. "Why don't you come?" he seemed to ask. He started off again.

"Here, Rover," called Jack, and he quickly took the end of Rover's tail in his hand. "Hang on to my arm," Jack yelled to Ronny.

Rover gave one little bark as if to say "Good!" And on went Rover, Jack, and Ronny.

The boys could hardly see at times. But not once did Rover stop, and not once did Jack let go of Rover's tail.

At last they came to a gate, and then to the house.

They were hungry, cold, and tired. But not one bite did they take till Rover had a big dinner in front of the fire.

Think About It

1. What problem did Jack and Ronny have?
2. Who helped them with their problem? What did he do?
3. Do you like Rover? Why?
4. What did the boys do to thank Rover?

Whenever a snowflake leaves the sky,
It turns and turns to say, "Good-by!
Good-by, dear cloud, so cool and gray!"
Then lightly travels on its way.

–Mary Mapes Dodge

Words to Watch For

kind   mind

washes   child

Two Dogs

One day two dogs met on the street. One of them was clean and looked well. His name was Jack. The other dog was not clean, and he was very thin. His name was Jip.

Jip said, "You look well and happy."

Jack said, "My master feeds me. He is very kind to me. Who feeds you?"

"My master feeds me sometimes," said Jip. "But sometimes he forgets. My master is not good to me. He is cross, and I am afraid of him."

"That is too bad," said Jack. "Masters should be kind to their dogs."

"How clean you are!" said Jip. "How do you keep so clean?"

Jack said, "My master washes me and gives me a clean bed to sleep on."

Jip said, "My master does not wash me, and I have no bed. I sleep anywhere I can find a spot. Sometimes I sleep in the house, and sometimes I sleep out in the cold or rain."

Jack said, "That's not right. Masters should wash their dogs and give them clean beds. I don't mind working for a child who is kind to me."

Just then the dogs heard a boy coming.

Jip said, "Wow! Here comes a boy. It may be my master. I wish I could climb a tree to get away from him."

Jack said, "Bow! Here comes a boy. It is my master. Let's run to meet him."

Something to Talk About

1. Which dog loved his master better, Jip or Jack?

   Why?

2. Do you have a pet? What kind of pet do you have? How do you take care of it?

3. Do you think that a person who is mean to animals will be kind to people? Why not?

The Bible Says

"A righteous man regardeth the life of his beast."

–Proverbs 12:10

Words to Watch For

journey   through   very   daily

A **journey** is a trip.

Daily means every day.

The Wind
and the Duck

On a very cold day of winter, North Wind started out on his daily journey. As he was blowing over a lake, he saw a lonely duck diving through the few holes left in the ice.

The duck was finding fish to eat.

"How foolish," blew the North Wind, "to try to win out over me. Why, I have chased every living thing away."

As he spoke, North Wind blew so hard that he froze over all the holes. Then the poor little duck had to hunt for a place on shore away from the wind.

Pleased with what he had done, the wind went away for the evening.

But the next morning when the wind arose, he found to his surprise that the duck had found some new holes. As he watched the duck, he saw him push the reeds aside and dive down into the water. Up he came with a big fish in his bill.

"This will never do," howled North Wind. "No duck is going to get the better of me."

For a whole week the wind blew harder and colder every day.

But each morning when he arose, he found the little duck at his work. Wind or no wind, the little duck was out on the ice, hunting new holes or breaking through the old ones.

At last North Wind said to himself: "Well, there is no getting ahead of that duck. He has made up his mind

what to do, and no one can stop him.
I shall let him alone."

Do You Know?

1. Why did the duck need to dive into the lake?
2. Was it easy for the duck to hunt for new holes every day?
3. What would have happened if the duck had said, "This is too hard. I give up"?
4. Why did the duck finally win over the North Wind?

Words to Watch For

carried   dove

A **dove** is a small, white bird.

The Ant
and the Dove

Once a little ant fell into a brook. She tried and tried to get out, but she could not. The brook carried her along.

"Help! Help!" she cried.

A bird was in a tree beside the brook. This bird was called a dove. The dove saw the little ant and felt sorry for her. He picked a leaf and dropped it into the brook.

"Here is a leaf, little ant. Climb on it and you will be safe," he said.

The ant climbed on the leaf, and the wind blew it along like a little boat. By and by it came to the shore. The ant crawled off the leaf and up the bank.

"Thank you, kind dove," she said.
"I hope I can help you some day."

One day a hunter came to the
woods. He saw the dove sitting in a
tree and was going to shoot him.

The dove did not see the hunter,
but the little ant saw him. She ran
to the hunter and bit his foot. This
made him jump, and he could not
shoot the dove.

The dove flew away and was safe.
As he flew away, he sang, "Thank
you, little ant. You have saved my
life."

Think About It

1. What problem did the ant have?
2. Who helped her? How did he do it?
3. What problem did the dove have?
4. Who helped the dove? How did she do it?
5. Were the ant and the dove good friends? Why do you think so?
6. Which sentences tell how to have good friends?

> Be kind.
> Be helpful.
> Be selfish.
> Be thankful.

The Bible Says

"A man that hath friends must show himself friendly; and there is a friend that sticketh closer than a brother.

—Proverbs 18:24

Words to Watch For

quarrel   caught

A **quarrel** is a fight.

The Lion
and the Bear

A lion and a bear caught the same fawn and had a quarrel over it. "It is mine," said the lion. "I killed it with my strong jaws."

"It is mine," said the bear. "I killed it with my strong paws."

They were so weak that they lay upon the ground panting and looking at each other.

A fox who was going by saw them with the dead fawn. He ran up to them, took the fawn in his mouth, and then ran away to his home.

"We should not quarrel," said the lion.

"It was all your fault," said the bear. "See, the fox has the fawn that we caught."

"If it had not been for this quarrel, we would have had a nice meal," said the lion.

The fox, as he lay upon the lawn eating the fawn, said, "If it had not been for that quarrel, I would not be eating this nice meal."

Do You Know?

1. What is a quarrel?
2. What were the lion and the bear quarreling over?
3. Which one do you think was right? Or do you think they were both right?
4. How could they have solved their problem without quarreling?
5. Whose fault was it that the fox got the fawn?

The Bible Says

"Depart from evil, and do good; seek peace, and pursue it."

–Psalm 34:14

Two and One

I have two ears and only one mouth;
    The reason, I think, is clear:
It teaches me that it will not do
    To talk about all I hear.

I have two eyes and only one mouth;
    The reason of this must be,
That I should learn it will not do
    To talk about all I see.

I have two hands and only one mouth;
    And it is worth repeating:
The two are for work that I need to do—
    The one is for eating.

Words to Watch For

rooster   weather vane   steeple

A **weather vane** is a piece of metal that tells which way the wind is blowing. Sometimes it looks like a **rooster.**

The Foolish Weather Vane

A rooster stood on the top of a tall steeple, but he did not crow.

He turned round and round and looked down at the little boats on the sea.

Early each morning, when the fishermen went down to the sea, they looked up at the rooster.

"Which way does the wind blow?" they said. And the weather vane told them.

If he pointed to the east, the men said, "We must not go to sea today." If he pointed to the west, they cried, "This is a good day to go fishing. Come, let us get the boats at once."

"The men do just as I tell them," thought the rooster. This made him very proud.

While he was thinking of this one night, the wind rushed by. "Point west!" it cried.

"Why should I point west?" thought the rooster. "I have always done just as the wind told me. I shall do so no longer."

"I stand here to tell the men when to take out their boats. Why should I obey the wind?"

"Point west!" said the wind. "Point west!" But the weather vane turned to the east.

The fishermen came down to the sea early in the morning. They took out their boats.

Just then one of the men cried, "There seems to be a west wind, but look! The rooster is pointed to the east. We must not go to sea."

So they stayed at home, but the sun was bright, and no storm came up all day.

"What is the matter with the weather vane?" they said. "We might have gone to sea, after all."

In the night the wind cried to the rooster, "Point east! Point east! A storm is coming."

"No," said the rooster, and he pointed to the west.

The fishermen came down to the beach in the morning, but only a few went out in their boats.

"Why do not all the men obey me?" thought the proud weather vane.

Soon a storm came up, and the boats were driven to the shore. The men would have been drowned if their friends had not helped them.

Now the proud rooster was sad.

"I wish that I had obeyed the wind," said he. "After this, I will always do as I am told."

But it was too late. The fishermen never looked at him again, because they could not believe what he told them.

Now a new weather vane stands on another steeple, and the men look at him every morning, for he always obeys the wind.

Do You Know?

1. What is a weather vane?
2. Why was the weather vane proud?
3. What did the weather vane decide to do?
4. Did the weather vane obey? Did it tell the truth?
5. Why didn't the men ever look at the weather vane again?
6. When is the best time to obey?

The Bible Says

"If ye be willing and obedient, ye shall eat of the fruit of the land."

–Isaiah 1:19

Who Has Seen the Wind?

Who has seen the wind?
    Neither I nor you:
But when the leaves hang trembling,
    The wind is passing through.
Who has seen the wind?
    Neither you nor I:
But when the trees bow down their heads,
    The wind is passing by.

–Christina Rossetti

Funny Bunny

Funny Bunny was asleep under a tree. All at once, he woke up and thought, "What if the world should break up? Then what would become of me?"

Just then, some monkeys dropped a coconut. It fell on the ground behind Funny Bunny.

Hearing the noise, the rabbit said to himself, "The earth is all breaking up!"

And he jumped up and ran just as fast as he could, without even looking back to see what had made the noise.

Another rabbit saw him running and called after him, "Why are you running so fast?"

"Don't ask me!" he cried.

But the other rabbit ran after him, begging to know what was the matter.

Funny Bunny said, "Don't you know? The earth is all breaking up!"

On he ran, and the second rabbit ran with him.

The next rabbit they met ran with them when he heard that the earth was all breaking up.

One rabbit after another joined them, until there were hundreds of rabbits running as fast as they could go.

They passed a deer and called out to him that the earth was all breaking up. The deer ran with them, too.

The deer called to a fox to come along, because the earth was all breaking up.

On and on they ran, and an elephant joined them.

At last the lion saw the animals running and heard their cry that the earth was all breaking up.

He thought there must be some mistake, so he ran to the foot of a hill in front of them and roared three times.

This stopped them, for they knew the voice of the King of Beasts, and they feared him.

"Why are you running so fast?" asked the lion.

"Oh, King Lion," they answered him, "the earth is all breaking up!"

"Who saw it breaking up?" asked the lion.

"I didn't," said the elephant. "Ask the fox—he told me about it."

"I didn't," said the fox.

"The rabbits told me about it," said the deer.

One after another of the rabbits said, "I did not see it, but another rabbit told me about it."

At last the lion came to Funny Bunny.

"Is it true that the earth is all breaking up?" the lion asked.

"Yes, O Lion, it is," said Funny Bunny. "I was asleep under a tree. I woke up and thought, 'What would become of me if the earth should all break up?' At that very moment, I heard the sound of the earth breaking up, and I ran away."

"Then," said the lion, "you and I will go back to the place where the earth began to break up and see what is the matter."

So the lion put Funny Bunny on his back, and away they went like the wind. The other animals waited for them at the foot of the hill.

Funny Bunny told the lion when they were near the place where he slept, and the lion saw just where the rabbit had been sleeping.

He saw, too, the coconut that had fallen to the ground near by. Then the lion said to Funny Bunny, "It must have been the sound of the coconut falling to the ground that you heard, you funny rabbit!"

And the lion ran back to the other animals and told them all about it.

If it had not been for the wise King of Beasts, they might be running still.

Think!

1. What did Funny Bunny think of when he woke up? Do you think he was wise? Why not?

2. What made the noise? What did Funny Bunny think made the noise?

3. What should Funny Bunny have done before he began to run?

4. Why did the other animals begin to run? Were they wise to run without making sure that something was wrong?

5. Who was the wisest animal of all? Why do you think so?

The Bible Says

"Happy is the man that findeth wisdom, and the man that getteth understanding."

–Proverbs 3:13

Words to Watch For

only   shining   everywhere

Tommy
and the Crows

"I will not go to school today," said Tommy. "I'll stay in the green fields and have a good time." So he sat down on a soft green bank under a tree. The sun was shining in a clear sky. Birds were singing everywhere.

"I will not go to school. I do not like my books. Besides, this bank is softer than the seats in the school-house."

Just as he said this, he looked up into a tree and saw some crows on one of the branches. One of them was hard at work making a nest with sticks.

"Here's a lazy boy!" said one of the crows. "He says he will not go to school." Then they all began to say,

"Caw! caw! caw!" as if they were making fun of Tommy.

"Well! What do you think of my work?" said the crow. "Look at my fine nest. What do you think of it, sir?"

"It is nice, Mr. Crow," said Tommy, "but I would not like to live in it."

"You would not? Well, you are only a boy and not as wise as a crow," said his new friend. The other crows cried, "Caw! caw! caw!" as if they thought so, too.

"Do you know why a crow is wiser than a silly boy?" asked the crow, putting his head on one side and looking at Tommy with his bright, black eye.

"No," said Tommy. "I thought boys were wiser than crows."

"You thought!" said the crow. "That shows how much you know about it. Tell me, can you make a house for yourself?"

"No, not now, but when I am a man I can."

"Why can't you do it now?" said the crow, turning his head to the other side.

"Why, I have not learned how to make one," said the little boy.

"Ho! ho!" said the crow, flapping his wings. "He has to wait till he learns how to make a house. He's a lazy boy!"

All the crows when they heard this cried, "Caw! caw! caw!"

"No one taught me how to make my house," said the crow. "Just look at it; what a nice house it is. I got all the sticks myself. But I do not mind hard work. I am not like a little boy that I know."

"But there are many things in this world besides houses," said Tommy.

"Yes, indeed," said the crow; "I was just thinking so. You need a coat as well as a house."

"That I do," said Tommy, "and I need a new one now. But you crows can't wear coats."

"Who told you that?" said the crow. "Look at my coat and tell me if you ever saw a finer one than this black coat of mine. Could you make such a fine black coat as this?"

"No," said Tommy, "but I can learn."

"Yes, yes, you can learn, but that is the way with all silly boys; you must be taught everything that you are to do."

Tommy felt that the crow had the best of it.

"Dear me," he said, "I never thought that crows were so wise."

"You may well say that," said the crow, who, with two others, was now sitting on a branch of the tree.

"You may well say that, Master Tom, but there is more for you to learn yet. How about your food? Where do you get that?"

"Why, my mother gets that for me. I find it on the table every day."

"You are a baby, then?"

"No, indeed," said Tommy. "I'll throw this stone at you if you don't watch what you say."

"Boys should never throw stones," said the crow. "I only asked if you were a baby. When a crow can go alone, he gets his own food."

"I will do that when I grow up," said Tommy. "I will learn how."

"Dear me," said the crow, "you will have much to learn before you are as wise as a crow."

"That may be so," said Tommy, hanging his head in shame, "but there is time for me to learn."

"You are a fine boy to come here and sit all day on the grass. Pick up your books and go to school! go to school! go to school! go to school!"

Then all the crows made such a noise that Tommy picked up his books to throw them at the crows. But they were off to another tree, where they all cried, "Caw! caw! caw!" till poor Tommy could not stand it any longer.

He held his books tightly and ran off to school as fast as his legs could take him.

Do You Know?

1. Why didn't Tommy want to go to school? Was he wise?
2. What three things can crows do that Tommy could not do?
3. How do crows know how to build nests?
4. What did God help people to build so children could learn?
5. Are you glad that Tommy went to school? Why?

The Bible Says

"A wise man will hear, and will increase learning."

–Proverbs 1:5

Words to Watch For

soldier   America   country
George Washington

George Washington was the first President of the United States.

George Washington

When George Washington was a boy, he lived on a farm. He went to a log schoolhouse in a field.

George was a good boy, and everybody trusted him. He liked to play soldier. He was the leader of the other boys. He was so kind and good that they did everything he told them.

George had a bright coat. He had a soldier's cap. He could drill the boys well, and the boys liked to have him drill them.

George was a brave, strong boy. He could ride a horse as well as any man. He could jump higher than any other boy in school.

George had a good, kind mother. She was his best teacher. She wanted him to be pure and upright. She told him many things which would help him to become a good man.

When George became a man, he liked to hunt and fish. He could play a nice tune on a flute. He liked to play the flute to amuse his mother.

When Washington became a man, he was a very brave soldier. He went to fight for our country. Many brave men went with him to fight for our country. The men made America a free country, and George Washington became the first President of our United States.

All boys should do as Washington did:

"Do your best, your very best,
And do it every day."

Lincoln and His Dog

Words to Watch For

moving   shoes

Abraham Lincoln

Abraham Lincoln was our sixteenth President. He was a good, honest man.

When Abraham Lincoln was a boy, he lived in a little log cabin. His family was very poor.

One day his father said, "Some of our friends are moving to a better place. Let us sell our farm and go with them."

So one morning the Lincoln family put all their goods into a big covered wagon and started for their new home.

Two oxen drew the heavy wagon. It was hard work. The roads were bad. There were hills to climb and streams to cross. It was a long, hard trip.

Little Abe's mother and sister rode in the covered wagon. Abe and his father walked beside the oxen, and their little dog ran along with them.

One very cold day they came to a stream. There was no bridge across it. It was covered with thin ice.

Abe and his father climbed into the wagon. The oxen drew it across the stream. Their feet broke through the ice at every step. At last they came to the other side.

Just then Abe heard a loud bark. He looked back and saw his dog on the other side of the stream.

Little Abe called and called, but the dog would not come. He was afraid to cross on the ice. Someone said, "We shall have to go on without him. We can't go back for him."

Little Abe said nothing. He sat down and took off his shoes and his stockings. Then he stepped into the cold water and waded across the stream to his dog.

The happy little dog jumped up and wagged his tail. He barked and barked, as if to say, "I was sure you would come for me, my kind master."

Abe picked him up and carried him across the stream to the rest of the family.

The Story of Moses

Words to Watch For

Egypt	Pharaoh	Miriam
Aaron	bulrushes	women

A Baby Is Born

One time God's people were in the land of Egypt. The ruler of Egypt was called the Pharaoh.

The Pharaoh did not love God. He hated God's people.

"I must get rid of those people," he said. "If I don't, they might fight my people."

So the Pharaoh said to his soldiers, "Go and find all the baby boys and throw them into the river!"

The soldiers marched to the town where God's people lived. They knocked on the doors of the houses. And every baby boy that they found, they threw into the river.

Moses' family was very sad. "What will we do with our little Moses?"

they said. "We love our baby. We don't want anyone to throw him into the river."

"I know!" said sister Miriam. "Let's hide him where no one can find him. Then he will be safe."

"Good," said the mother. And she hid little Moses in a safe place in the house.

"Now no one can hurt our baby," said brother Aaron. "God will take care of him and keep him safe."

A Strange Boat

For three months the family kept the baby hidden.

But then something happened. Little Moses was getting bigger. It was hard to keep him quiet.

"What can we do, Mother?" said Miriam. "The soldiers will hear him."

"I'm afraid," said Aaron. "I don't want the soldiers to throw our baby into the river."

"Don't be afraid," said Mother. "God will take care of Moses. I have a plan. Will you help me, Miriam? Will you help me, Aaron?"

"Oh, yes, Mother," said Miriam and Aaron. "We will do anything that you say."

"Then come with me down to the river," she said. And down to the river they went.

"See those long grasses in the river?" said Mother. "Those are bulrushes. Come and help me pick them."

"This is hard, but it's fun," said Miriam. "I like to work for Mother. I want to help our Baby Moses."

Soon Mother, Miriam, and Aaron each had a big bundle of bulrushes.

"We can stop now," said Mother. "Now I need to do something at home."

Miriam and Aaron carried the bulrushes home. Then they sat and watched Mother.

Mother was making something with the bulrushes.

"What is it?" said Miriam.

"What is it?" said Aaron.

Soon Mother held up a little basket. "This is for Baby Moses," she said. "But it is not done yet."

Mother found some thick, sticky tar. She rubbed the tar all over the basket. "Now, no water can get in," she said.

"Water?" said Miriam.

"Water?" said Aaron.

"Yes, water," said Mother. "Let me get Baby Moses, and then we must go back down to the river."

"Now I see!" said Aaron. "The basket will be a boat for Moses. We can hide him in the river!"

"That's right," said Mother. "Come along, now." And back to the river they went.

Mother put Moses into the basket. She put a cover on the basket. Then she put the basket into the river.

A Hard Job

"I can hardly see him, now," said Aaron. "The bulrushes make a good hiding place."

"Now I have a hard job for some-one," said Mother. "Miriam, can you do a hard job?"

"Oh, yes," said Miriam. "I can work hard."

"Miriam," said Mother, "I have to go home. I need someone to watch the baby. Will you stay here and watch Moses?"

"Oh, Mother!" said Miriam. "I will be afraid. I don't want to stay alone."

"God will be with you," said Mother. "You are not alone, Miriam. God will help you to be brave."

"That's right!" said Miriam. "I will stay, Mother. God will help me take care of Moses."

"Good-by, Miriam," said Aaron.

"Good-by," said Mother. "God will help you, Miriam."

Mother and Aaron went home. Now Miriam was alone with the baby.

"Please, God," said Miriam. "Don't let anything hurt Baby Moses. I know You will take care of him."

Miriam looked up. Someone was coming!

Was it the Pharaoh? Was it the soldiers?

No, it was some women.

"Why, it's the princess!" thought Miriam. "It's the Pharaoh's daughter. What will she do to our baby? Will she hurt him?"

A Happy Ending

Down to the water came the princess with her maids.

"Look!" said the princess. "I see something in the water. Go get it for me, maid."

A maid went into the water. Soon
she came back with Moses in the
basket.

"What will happen now?" thought Miriam. "Please, God, take care of Baby Moses."

The maid took the basket to the princess. The princess took the cover off. And Baby Moses began to cry!

"Oh, look," said the princess. "What a sweet baby! I want to help this baby."

Now Miriam knew that she must be brave. She must talk to the princess!

Miriam walked right up to the princess. "I know someone who can help you take care of the baby," said Miriam. "Shall I go get her?"

"Go," said the princess.

And where do you suppose Miriam went? She went right back to her own home!

"Mother, Mother!" she cried. "The princess found Baby Moses. She will not hurt him. She wants you to take care of him until he is big."

Mother ran to the river to find the princess.

"Will you take care of this baby?" said the princess. "Will you take him home with you until he is big?"

"Oh, yes!" said Mother. "I will take good care of this baby."

The happy mother went home with her own Baby Moses. She took care of Moses, and God helped her.

Moses grew to be a big, strong boy. His mother taught him to love God. Then he went to the palace to live with the princess.

Moses learned many things in the palace. When he became a man, God chose him to be a great leader of his people.

Moses had a hard job to do. But he always could say, "God is my helper. God will take care of me."

Phonics Word Lists

With Definitions and Practice Sentences

 A. *Students should practice these words before reading "Sunshine and Rain," p. 9.*

1. -ed in wanted

want – wanted	planted	floated
land – landed	dented	sounded
add – added	shouted	sorted

2. -ed in looked

look – looked	crashed	mixed
talk – talked	smashed	thanked
help – helped	splashed	packed

3. -ed in played

play – played	stayed	sighed
yell – yelled	joined	snowed
boil – boiled	bailed	enjoyed

4. Review of long words

happy	rabbit	secret	student
butter	jacket	polite	handle
middle	Bible	tickle	silver

B. *Read before "Ready to Go," p. 11.*

1. **wh** in **wh**ale, **wh** in **wh**o

whale	which	whole	what	when
wheel	whose	who	where	somewhere

What game do you like to play?

Who is your best friend?

2. Review of -ed

sifted	pleased	sailed	surprised	picked
milked	rained	helped	dressed	whimpered

3. Review of the suffixes -s, -ing, -ed

yell	sound	run	bump	whack
yells	sounds	runs	bumps	whacks
yelling	sounding	running	bumping	whacking
yelled	sounded	ran	bumped	whacked

Do not make a **sound.**

That **sounds** like a train.

I am **sounding** out the word.

John's song **sounded** pretty.

C. *Read before "Mr. Rabbit and Tar Baby," p. 17.*

1. tch in patch
(This spelling usually comes after a short vowel.)

Mitch	fetch	ditch	stretch
watch	catch	hitch	sketch
kitchen	latch	match	crutch

2. Short-vowel words in which the consonant is doubled before adding a suffix beginning with a vowel.

pad	hop	pat	shred	slam
padded	hopped	patted	shredded	slammed
padding	hopping	patting	shredding	slamming

D. *Read before "Mr. Rabbit Gets Away," p. 21.*

1. Long words that can be divided between two vowels. (Remember that the vowel at the end of the syllable will usually be long.)

lion	quiet	poet	brier	duet
diet	cruel	poem	create	video

Create means to make something out of nothing. "In the beginning God **created** the heaven and the earth." (Genesis 1:1)

2. Words in which silent *e* is dropped before adding a suffix beginning with a vowel.

fade	like	save	drape	live
fading	liking	saving	draping	living
faded	liked	saved	draped	lived
skating	smiled	grading	shaping	trading

Read before "Grandmother's Path," p. 27.

ear in **ear**, ear in b**ear**, ear in **ear**th

hear	bear	earn	clear	pearl
fear	pear	learn	near	search

"**Swear** not at all." (Matthew 5:34)
"I will **hear** what God the Lord will speak." (Psalm 85:8)
"My God, **early** will I seek Thee." (Psalm 63:1)

F. *Read before "Why Jimmy Did His Work,"*
p. 35.

1. **old** in g**old**, **mb** in la**mb**

bold	told	comb	climbing	scolded
cold	old	climb	sold	holds

2. Review of words with suffixes.

rate	comb	pick	skin	fear	part
rates	combs	picks	skins	fears	parts
rated	combed	picked	skinned	feared	parted
rating	combing	picking	skinning	fearing	parting

My mother will **comb** my hair.
I like the way she **combs** it.
Yesterday she **combed** it behind my ears.
I am **combing** it right now.

G. *Read before "Dotty and Spotty," p. 43.*

1. **ew** in fl**ew, ew** in f**ew**

new	flew	knew	dew	crew
stew	grew	jewel	blew	newspaper

2. **Review of long words and words with suffixes.**

poem	tickled	spider	frowning	opened
fuel	beside	chewing	swimming	pocket

H. *Read before "A Brave Dog," p. 49.*

1. **-en** in sharp**en, -y** in rain**y, -er** in bigg**er, -ly** in slow**ly**

quick – quicken	sand – sandy	quick – quickly
gold – golden	cold – colder	light – lightly
breeze – breezy	jump – jumper	sudden – suddenly

2. **Review of the suffixes -s, -ing, -ed, -y, -er, -ly, and -en.**

cloudy	blowing	quietly	shouted	forgotten
shouts	skater	proudly	invited	explaining
loudly	sharply	rider	loosen	happened

I. *Read before "Two Dogs," p. 55.*

1. **ild** in ch**ild**, **ind** in k**ind**, **mb** in la**mb**

wild	wind	find	behind	childhood
mild	mind	climbing	kindly	reminding

2. **-es** in peach**es**

fish – fishes	brush – brushes	express – expresses
rose – roses	nurse – nurses	peach – peaches
fox – foxes	mix – mixes	class – classes

J. *Read before "The Wind and the Duck," p. 59.*

1. **c** in **c**ity (**c** before e, i, or y says "*s.*")

cent	cider	Nancy	cancel	space shuttle
rice	city	city center	circle	spacecraft
grace	fancy	silence	center	spice rack

races	succeed	fence	principle	bicycle
places	pencil	decide	Pacific	Joyce

Center means middle.

Glance means to look quickly at something.

Pronounce means to say.

2. Review of the suffixes -ed, -er, -ing, and -ly.

started	harder	daily	finding	blowing
watched	colder	lonely	howled	pleased
diving	chased	living	breaking	getting

K. Read before "The Ant and the Dove," p. 63.

1. au in faucet, aw in saw

cause	fault	sauce	because	astronaut
haul	jaw	crawled	faucet	launch

An **author** is someone who writes books.

Autumn is the season that comes between summer and winter. Sometimes we call it the fall.

2. ea in leaf, ea in thread, ea in steak

beach	thread	break	leather	eastern
repeat	dead	yea	weather	head
teacher	feather	great	yeast	peanut

Repeat means to say again.

If we like something, we say that it is **pleasant.**

L. *Read before "The Foolish Weather Vane,"
p. 71.*

1. **ie** in brown**ie**

niece	yield	shriek	achieve	pieces
cookies	fields	briefly	belief	believe
Tammie	thief	grief	shrieking	yielding
yielded	shields	believed	relieved	achievement

I **believe** that the Bible is God's Word.

This is my **belief.**

2. **ey** in k**ey**, **ey** in ob**ey**

keyhole	they	valley	donkey	jersey
kidney	preys	obeyed	journey	chimney
obeying	keys	jockeys	surveyed	New Jersey
valleys	barley	turkey	survey	parsley

A **donkey** went on a long **journey** over hill and **valley.**

"Children, **obey** your parents in all things."
(Colossians 3:20)

M. *Read before "Funny Bunny," p. 77.*

1. **o** in sh**o**vel

some	done	love	company	discover
glove	dove	lemon	become	wondering
front	oven	honey	monkey	compass
month	none	money	blossom	computer
won	son	pilot	above	customer

A **kingdom** is a land ruled by a king.

Handsome means good-looking.

Complete means to finish.

Wisdom means being wise.
"The fear of the Lord is the beginning
of **wisdom**." (Proverbs 9:10)

2. **ph** in **ph**one

phone	elephant	phonics	phrase
graph	gopher	alphabet	photo

A **photograph** is a picture taken with a camera.

A **phonograph** is a record player.

A **phrase** is a part of a sentence.

N. *Read before "Tommy and the Crows," p. 85.*

1. **ch** in **ch**orus

chord	ache	Christ	Christmas	stomach
chorus	echo	anchor	headache	school

2. **ough**t in th**ough**t, **augh**t in c**augh**t

bought	ought	taught	thought	haughty
brought	fought	caught	daughter	naughty

O. *Read before "George Washington," p. 93.*

1. **g** in **g**iant (**g** before e, i, or y says *"j."*)

cage	stage	gem	register	refrigerate
page	strange	gentle	energy	ginger
wage	age	germ	George	giant

Egypt is a country in Africa.

Gigantic means **huge,** or very, very big.

Have you ever heard of the **Gingerbread** Man?

2. dge in fu**dge**
(This spelling usually comes after a short vowel.)

badge	ledge	ridges	fudge	dodger
badger	wedge	pledge	porridge	lodger

A **hedge** is a row of bushes that make a fence.

Madge and **Midge** went over the **bridge.**

Trudge means to walk and walk.

I **pledge** allegiance to the flag.

P. *Read before "Lincoln and His Dog," p. 95.*

a- in **a**sleep, **al-** in **al**so, **be-** in **be**cause, **en-** in **en**joy, and **un-** in **un**button

*(A **prefix** comes before a root word to change the meaning and make a new word.)*

enlist	because	ahead	altogether	unbutton
encircle	become	alone	almost	unkind
enjoy	belong	afar	always	unglue

Q. *Read before "The Story of Moses," p. 99.*

1. Review of the suffixes -ed, -ing, -en, -ly, and -es.

knock – knocked	hiding	hated
live – lived	hidden	making
happen – happened	houses	coming
watch – watched	grasses	believes
learn – learned	ladies	rivers

2. Review of prefixes and long words.

along	people	quiet	happen	cover
began	every	river	anything	princess
until	family	bundle	someone	palace
also	object	water	understand	Pharaoh

The **princess** lived in **Egypt.**

The king of **Egypt** is called a **Pharaoh.**